Say the sounds and blend them together to read the word.

camp

Look at the letters and say the sounds. See how quickly you can say all of them.

Say the word *map* and listen out for the sounds: *map* – /m-a-p/. (There is one sound dot underneath the map for each sound in the word.)